1001
Things to Find

1 owl

3 ghosts

2 black cats

4 bats

5 bones

Spooky

igloobooks

Can you find 1001 spooky things?

The ghosts and ghouls are out to play and it's time for a creepy finding adventure! Wendy Witch and Vampire Vlad are on their way to the big Monster Ball. They must collect all 14 party invitations along the way, plus lots of other gruesome hidden objects. Help them journey through Spookyville to get to the party, if you dare!

Wendy Witch

Vampire Vlad

Party invitation

On the opposite page, see if you can spot Wendy Witch, Vampire Vlad and a party invitation. Once you've found them, see if you can spot the items below, too.

7 candleholders

9 jars of eyeballs

14 chipped teacups

Haunted Mansion

Vlad and Wendy are leaving their spooky mansion and can't wait to start their adventure! Can you find them and a party invitation hidden in the scene below?

3 grandfather clocks

4 chained ghouls

5 suits of armour

6 headless butlers

7 dusty portraits

8 stone busts

9 piles of books

10 golden candelabras

13 sneaky spiders

16 white mice

Ghoulish Graveyard

OOO! Ghoulish Graveyard is full of creepy ghosts and monsters! An invitation is hidden somewhere. Can you spot it, plus Vlad and Wendy, too?

3 blue ghosts

4 old tombs

5 zombie hands

6 glass lanterns

7 black ravens

8 mummies in top hats

9 stripy snakes

10 zombie girls

13 beast faces

16 spotty moths

UFO Crash Site

The friends head off through the dark forest, but it isn't long before they stumble across a top-secret alien crash site! Where are Vlad, Wendy and an invitation?

4 pop-up tents

6 orange aliens

7 masked scientists

10 monkey aliens

14 alien bugs

Pumpkin Patch

After getting through all that gooey alien slime, Vlad and Wendy visit Frightful Farm to join in with a quick pumpkin competition. Can you spot them and an invitation?

4 red wheelbarrows

6 silly scarecrows

7 demon rabbits

10 purple pumpkins

14 pointy trowels

Frightful Funfair

There's just enough time before the party for some fun at the fair. Hold on tight and get ready to scream! Can you find Wendy and Vlad, plus an invitation?

3 zombie teddies

4 blue rubber ducks

5 ride operators

6 broken windows

7 naughty rats

8 sticks of candyfloss

9 skull balloons

10 orange wristbands

13 yeti footprints

16 black toffee apples

Ancient Ruins

The crumbling ancient ruins are full of lost explorers, monsters and zombies. Let's hope Vlad and Wendy don't get lost, too! Find them and then look for the invitation.

3 fallen statues

4 zombie tribesmen

5 cheeky monkeys

6 old maps

7 pairs of red eyes

8 sharp arrows

9 explorer ghosts

10 scarab beetles

13 poisonous flowers

16 ancient coins

Stinking Swamp

Uh, oh! Vlad and Wendy have hit a dead end at a swamp. They need to escape before they get stuck and miss the party! Can you spot them and the invitation?

4 red rowing boats

6 hazardous waste drums

7 swamp monsters

10 toothed plants

14 blue lizards

Creepy Cave

Luckily, they spot a hidden tunnel leading down under the forest, through a dark, drippy cave. But where does it lead? Can you find Wendy and Vlad? Where is that invitation?

4 singing mermaids

6 rubber rings

7 piles of treasure

10 pink crystal clusters

14 vampire bats

Mysterious Museum

Vlad and Wendy follow the tunnel, which takes them to Spookyville Museum. It's full of creepy artefacts! Can you spot Vlad, Wendy and an invitation?

3 triceratops skeletons

4 ancient pharaohs

5 hairy cavemen

6 brown helmets

7 cursed necklaces

8 clay urns

9 withered hands

10 'Do Not Touch' signs

13 shrunken heads

16 museum tickets

Wacky Lab

Whoa! Vlad and Wendy have found a door to a secret lab. They'd better escape before someone uses them in an experiment! Can you spot them and an invitation?

4 green monsters

6 pickled brains

7 test-tube sets

10 pairs of safety goggles

14 radioactive cockroaches

Dark Dungeon

Vlad and Wendy squeeze through a hidden trapdoor and stop to cast some spooky spells in the dark dungeon. Where are they both? Can you see an invitation?

4 mops and buckets

6 flaming torches

7 slimy snails

10 spooky cards

14 pairs of handcuffs

Grisly Kitchen

Mmm! Something smells horrid. Perfect for a Monster Ball. Mouldy cheese, anyone? Can you see an invitation? Vlad and Wendy must be here somewhere.

3 rickety trolleys

4 bowls of rat-tail soup

5 smashed plates

6 plates of eyeball pasta

7 zombie waiters

8 slime smoothies

9 toothy tacos

10 mouldy cheeses

13 stinky fish bones

16 wiggly maggots

Monster Ball

They made it! Now it's time to boogie and have some fun. Can you find Vampire Vlad, Wendy Witch and one last invitation hidden among all the spooky party fun?

3 shiny necklaces

4 singing banshees

5 ghost piñatas

6 loud speakers

7 dancing mummies

8 party posters

9 floating candles

10 red handprints

13 glowing fireflies

16 orange balloons

Well done! You got Vampire Vlad and Wendy Witch to the Monster Ball! Now go back and see if you can find each of these spooky items in every scene, too.

A bottle of potion

A magic spell book

A green-flame candle

A magic crystal ball

A golden cobweb

A jewel-encrusted broomstick

Baelfire the bat

A witch's stripy sock

Were you looking closely? Each of these items is hidden in a different scene. Go back and see if you can find each one. They all appear only once in the book.

A zombie dog

A giant purple monster

A bearded wizard

A vampire wearing pumpkin shoes